Stan is R

Written by
Jill Atkins

Illustrated by
Daniel Strange

I went to the shop and I got Stan.

Stan had six arms with big hands and three legs with big feet.

It cost a lot of cash.

I am rich, so that was all right!

STAN
SOLD

"This is Stan," I said to my dad. "It will help me with a lot of things."

"We shall see," said Dad.

"Come with me," I said to Stan.

I took Stan up to my room.

"Help me. Get rid of all this rubbish,"
I said.

"Rubb-ish!" Stan said.

Stan took my lunchbox, my DVDs and my
bag.

They all went out onto the landing.

"Not my good things! Just the junk," I said to Stan.

"J-unk!" Stan said.

Stan took my books and they went out onto the landing, too.

"Not my books! Just the rubbish!" I said.

“Rub-bish!” Stan said.

Stan kept picking things up. They all went out onto the landing.

“Stop! You are not picking up rubbish or junk.” I said.

“Rubb-ish! J-unk!” Stan said.

It did not stop.

Next, my bed went out onto the landing.

“Not my bed! I sleep on that!” I said.

The room was empty.

But no! It was not empty.

The carpet was still there.

Stan took up the carpet. It went out onto the landing.

"I cannot stand this!" I said. "Come with me."

I took Stan down to see Dad.

"So is Stan helping you?" Dad asked.

"No! That is it! I quit! Stan must go!" I said.

I took Stan
back to the shop.

Then I had to sort all my things. It took a week to sort them all.

I do not need Stan!

Not for all the cash in the bank!